Dr Sprocket
Makes a Rocket

KU-042-467

Dr Sprocket makes a rocket.
She makes it from old boxes.
She makes it from old cans.

She makes it from computers.
She makes it from old pans.

She makes it from old chairs.
She makes it from old wires.

She makes it from old clocks.
She makes it from old tyres.

She makes it
from old buckets.

She starts it with a broom.

7

Dr Sprocket flies her rocket.
Zoo-oo-oom!

8

The Greedy Gobbler

"I am the greedy gobbler,"
the vacuum cleaner sang.

It gobbled up the dust.
It gobbled up the mat.

It gobbled up the chair.
It gobbled up the cat.

It gobbled up the cups.
It gobbled up the plates.

It gobbled up the ball.
It gobbled up the skates.

"I am the greedy gobbler,"
the vacuum cleaner sang.

It tried to gobble up
the bed.
BANG!

The Wind

The wind
blew the balloon away.

It blew the balloon
over the lake.

It blew the balloon
over the trees.

It blew the balloon
over the cars.

It blew the balloon
over the house.

Then. . .
the wind stopped,
and the balloon came down.

"Happy birthday,
Grandfather!"